"The Basketball Game

Welcome basketball fans, kids, parents, grammas and gramps.
Who will win this big game and be this year's new champs?

The Lizards are really strong and move as fast as lightning.
The green, white and black are tall and can be so frightening.

**SKYHAWKS
90**

**LIZARDS
90**

But the Skyhawks can leap so high, defying gravitation.
The yellow, white and blue birds give a flying demonstation.

The score is tied at ninety, the teams play up and down the court.
The winner will need to score soon, as the time left is short.

Have fun watching the action, all eyes are on the play.
And practice your reading, to surprise someone today.

Make use of those red letters and blue words, a handy guide.
All the letters have sounds, that make words, along each side.

Practice early reading skills using the special page format.
- see the Literacy Guide chart on page 54 -
4 Building Blocks Of Reading - With Suggested Reading Skills Activities

Sports Action Kids Books - Book 4
ISBN-978-1-7771741-9-4

sportsactionbooks@gmail.com

Copyright © Coach Craig B.Ed. 2020

"Go Skyhawks! Fly-Sky-High!",
the fans cheer up in the stands.

A a
B b
C c
D d
E e
F f
G g
H h
I i
J j
K k
L l
M m
N n
O o
P p
Q q
R r
S s
T t
U u
V v
W w
X x
Y y
Z z

Standing at the side-line, a Skyhawk holds the ball and waits.

"Go! Lizards-Are-Wizards!",
others shout clapping their hands.

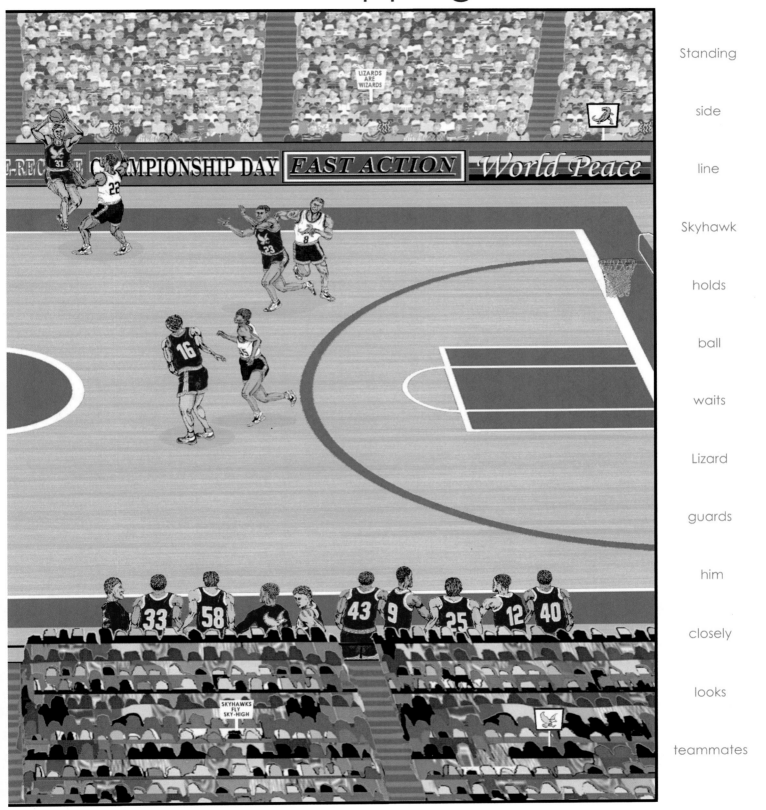

Standing side line Skyhawk holds ball waits Lizard guards him closely looks teammates

A Lizard guards him closely,
as he looks for his teammates.

A a
B b
C c
D d
E e
F f
G g
H h
I i
J j
K k
L l
M m
N n
O o
P p
Q q
R r
S s
T t
U u
V v
W w
X x
Y y
Z z

He sees a Hawk and throws the ball, to resume the action.

He
sees
throws
the
ball
to
resume
action
sprinting
Hawk
catches
with
quick
reaction

The sprinting Hawk catches
the ball, with a quick reaction.

A B C D E F G H I J K L M N O P Q R S T U V W X Y Z
a b c d e f g h i j k l m n o p q r s t u v w x y z

A Lizard guards the Skyhawk, and really concentrates.

he

A

Lizard

guards

Skyhawk

really

concentrates

and

the

dribbles

ball

then

stops

hesitates

The Hawk dribbles the ball,
then he stops and hesitates.

As the Lizard guards him,
the Hawk makes an arm pump.

the

Lizard

guards

him

makes

arm

pump

looks

up

basket

then

both

them

jump

He looks up to the basket,
then both of them jump.

A a
B b
C c
D d
E e
F f
G g
H h
I i
J j
K k
L l
M m
N n
O o
P p
Q q
R r
S s
T t
U u
V v
W w
X x
Y y
Z z

He shoots a jump shot,
the ball rises up and is drifting.

shoots

rises

jump

shot

drifting

flies

net

players

move

in

and

are

shifting

It flies to the net, the players
move in and are shifting.

A a
B b
C c
D d
E e
F f
G g
H h
I i
J j
K k
L l
M m
N n
O o
P p
Q q
R r
S s
T t
U u
V v
W w
X x
Y y
Z z

The ball bounces, with players jumping up and soaring high.

ball

bounces

jumping

up

players

soaring

high

Skyhawk

taps

finishing

try

ball

scoring

in

A Skyhawk taps the ball in, finishing the scoring try.

"Go Skyhawks! Fly-Sky-High!",
sing out some fans, all united.

A a
B b
C c
D d
E e
F f
G g
H h
I i
J j
K k
L l
M m
N n
O o
P p
Q q
R r
S s
T t
U u
V v
W w
X x
Y y
Z z

A Lizard dribbles the ball so fast,
with outstanding skill.

"Go! *Lizards-Are-Wizards!*", chant other fans, all excited.

dribbles

fast

skill

Lizard

outstanding

sprints

past

Skyhawk

and

leaves

quickly

standing

still

him

He sprints quickly past a Skyhawk, and leaves him standing still.

A a
B b
C c
D d
E e
F f
G g
H h
I i
J j
K k
L l
M m
N n
O o
P p
Q q
R r
S s
T t
U u
V v
W w
X x
Y y
Z z

He dribbles, then stops,
and a Lizard runs into his view.

view

dribbles

ball

then

Lizard

runs

net

looks

flips

him

pass

right

pushing

through

He looks to the net, then flips
the ball, passing it right through.

A a
B b
C c
D d
E e
F f
G g
H h
I i
J j
K k
L l
M m
N n
O o
P p
Q q
R r
S s
T t
U u
V v
W w
X x
Y y
Z z

The Lizard grabs the ball then dribbles, and shifts quickly by.

dribbles

then

Lizard

grabs

shifts

by

quickly

Leaping

while

stretching

arms

lifts

high

ball

Leaping up while stretching his arms, he lifts the ball high.

A	a
B	b
C	c
D	d
E	e
F	f
G	g
H	h
I	i
J	j
K	k
L	l
M	m
N	n
O	o
P	p
Q	q
R	r
S	s
T	t
U	u
V	v
W	w
X	x
Y	y
Z	z

He takes it up above the basket, trying hard to score.

takes

above

basket

trying

slams

score

two

then

score

while

points

flying

off

floor

Then slams it in for two points,
while flying off the floor.

A	a
B	b
C	c
D	d
E	e
F	f
G	g
H	h
I	i
J	j
K	k
L	l
M	m
N	n
O	o
P	p
Q	q
R	r
S	s
T	t
U	u
V	v
W	w
X	x
Y	y
Z	z

The Lizards move in to guard all
the Hawks, surrounding them.

guard

move

surrounding

Hawks

Lizards

lobs

all

them

Hawk

over

ball

who's

him

hounding

A Hawk lobs the ball over the Lizard, who's hounding him.

A a
B b
C c
D d
E e
F f
G g
H h
I i
J j
K k
L l
M m
N n
O o
P p
Q q
R r
S s
T t
U u
V v
W w
X x
Y y
Z z

Two Lizards move fast, double teaming the Hawk with the ball.

Two double teaming move Lizards with grips ball screaming fans hall Hawk tight fast

He grips the ball tight, to the screaming of fans in the hall.

A a
B b
C c
D d
E e
F f
G g
H h
I i
J j
K k
L l
M m
N n
O o
P p
Q q
R r
S s
T t
U u
V v
W w
X x
Y y
Z z

He twists to protect the ball, from the Lizards' half-court press.

twists

protect

ball

from

Lizards'

He

bounces

half-court

pass

off

press

floor

relieving

stress

He bounces a pass off the floor,
relieving all the stress.

A
B
C
D
E
F
G
H
I
J
K
L
M
N
O
P
Q
R
S
T
U
V
W
X
Y
Z

a
b
c
d
e
f
g
h
i
j
k
l
m
n
o
p
q
r
s
t
u
v
w
x
y
z

A Skyhawk takes the pass,
and dribbles the ball in control.

takes

pass

dribbles

control

Skyhawk

runs

fast

team

shot

give

for

next

field-goal

He runs fast, to give his team a shot for the next field-goal.

"Go Skyhawks! Fly-Sky-High!",
the fans cheer up in the stands.

A a
B b
C c
D d
E e
F f
G g
H h
I i
J j
K k
L l
M m
N n
O o
P p
Q q
R r
S s
T t
U u
V v
W w
X x
Y y
Z z

In the Lizard's zone he pivots,
seeing a man who's free.

"Go! Lizards-Are-Wizards!",
others shout clapping their hands.

zone

pivots

man

free

fires

chest

pass

him

top

key

seeing

who's

Lizard's

his

He fires a chest pass to him,
at the top of the key.

A a
B b
C c
D d
E e
F f
G g
H h
I i
J j
K k
L l
M m
N n
O o
P p
Q q
R r
S s
T t
U u
V v
W w
X x
Y y
Z z

©C.HICKS/96

He shoots the ball. A Lizard leaps
to block the scoring play.

shoots

leaps

block

scoring

reaches

knock

play

away

high

hand

to

Lizard

He

ball

The Lizard reaches his hand high, to knock the ball away.

A a
B b
C c
D d
E e
F f
G g
H h
I i
J j
K k
L l
M m
N n
O o
P p
Q q
R r
S s
T t
U u
V v
W w
X x
Y y
Z z

The players scramble after the ball, with such aggression.

players such scramble after aggression Lizard hustles grabs it regain ball with to possession

A Lizard hustles and grabs it, to regain possession.

A a
B b
C c
D d
E e
F f
G g
H h
I i
J j
K k
L l
M m
N n
O o
P p
Q q
R r
S s
T t
U u
V v
W w
X x
Y y
Z z

He fires a perfect pass
to a sprinting teammate.

fires

perfect

pass

sprinting

teammate

Lizard

Hawks

two

past

grabs

late

too

reaching

up

The Lizard grabs it, past two Hawks reaching up too late.

He dribbles to the basket,
then leaps trying for a lay-up.

dribbles

basket

leaps

then

trying

lay-up

ball

keeps

from

Hawks

as

flying

way

up

Holding the ball from the Hawks,
as he's flying on the way up.

A a
B b
C c
D d
E e
F f
G g
H h
I i
J j
K k
L l
M m
N n
O o
P p
Q q
R r
S s
T t
U u
V v
W w
X x
Y y
Z z

Aiming for the net, he laid the ball up as the crowd roared.

Aiming
net
laid
ball
the
crowd
falls
roared
after
up
bouncing
off
backboard
But

But the ball falls, after bouncing
up and off the backboard.

A a
B b
C c
D d
E e
F f
G g
H h
I i
J j
K k
L l
M m
N n
O o
P p
Q q
R r
S s
T t
U u
V v
W w
X x
Y y
Z z

©C.HICKS/96

The players jump for the rebound,
and they juggle for the ball.

players

jump

rebound

for

juggle

ball

wins

struggle

fast

lightning

Lizard

all

them

as

A Lizard as fast as lightning,
wins the struggle with them all.

A a
B b
C c
D d
E e
F f
G g
H h
I i
J j
K k
L l
M m
N n
O o
P p
Q q
R r
S s
T t
U u
V v
W w
X x
Y y
Z z

Two Skyhawks jump up again,
reaching to stop the leaping lizard.

Skyhawks

leaping

reaching

Lizard

high

stop

Two

jams

ball

just

like

wily

net

wizard

But he jams the ball into the net, just like a wily wizard.

Oh! Yeah! Wow! Alright!, shout some fans, they start an uproar!

The Lizards win, they jump and skip about, so happy and glad.

Oh! No! Geez! Oh-man!, pout other fans, they cheer no more!

Lizards

win

jump

skip

happy

glad

Skyhawks

stand

still

looking

sad

downcast

stand

silent

As the Skyhawks stand silent and still, looking downcast and sad.

Wow! What fun and excitement for the fans who came.
The Skyhawks and Lizards played an awesome game.

The players fought hard with no energy to spare.
In the heat of the battle they always played fair.

SKYHAWKS

92

LIZARDS

94

The players now walk about and greet one another.
They reach to fist pump, showing respect for each other.

Yes, winning the championship is a sensation.
And, playing with sportsmanship wins admiration.

Grown ups! Let's help the kids learn good reading skills.
Like athletes have coaches for good training drills.

The 4 building blocks of reading are shown in a chart.
Try some of the tips to help make the kids really smart.

Practice early reading skills using the special page format.
- see the Literacy Guide chart on page 54 -
4 Building Blocks Of Reading - With Suggested Reading Skills Activities

Basketball Player Positions

In the game of basketball there are five main positions. Each team will have two guards, two forwards, and a center on the court during a game. While all five players are able to play anywhere on the court at any given time, they do have some special roles to play during a game.

Point Guard

The point guard is often one of the fastest (and shorter) players on the team. They will often be the player who dribbles the ball up the court when a team goes on offense as the other players get into their positions. They are very skilled and are often the leader for a team during a game, calling out plays, and controlling the tempo of the game.

Shooting Guard

The shooting guard is usually taller than the point guard and often these players are the best shooters on a team from longer distances. While they are also very fast and good dribblers, their main job is to get open to receive a pass and then try a shot to score.

Center (Forward)

The player who usually plays center is often the tallest player on the team. Their main job is to gather in rebounds at both ends of the court. They will try to gather in offensive rebounds and try to score points at the other teams basket and then retrieve defensive rebounds when the play is at their own basket. They also will try to block shots taken by the other team to prevent them from scoring.

Power Forward

Like the center the power forward is one of the tallest players on the team. Their main job is to play by the basket and near the key (painted area) and then try to score with short-range shots, layups and dunks. Power forwards are also expected to do a lot of rebounding at both ends of the court.

Small Forward

The small forward is taller than the guards but not as big as the center or power forward. These players often have very good skills in shooting either from long range or near the basket with close in shots to score. They also help to get rebounds and control the ball.

The fans are so excited, on the edge of their seats!

A a
B b
C c
D d
E e
F f
G g
H h
I i
J j
K k
L l
M m
N n
O o
P p
Q q
R r
S s
T t
U u
V v
W w
X x
Y y
Z z

Each Lizard guards a Skyhawk and gets back to play defense.

And they are nervous, no time for cell phone calls or tweets!

Each Lizard guards Skyhawk gets back play defense Hawk guard dribbles ball set their offense

Referee
side-line
Shooting Guard
basketball net
free-throw line
Point Guard
Point Guard
key
center circle
basketball court
3-point line

The Hawk guard dribbles the ball as they set up their offense.

Basketball Glossary

Assist: A player earns an assist when they pass the ball to another player who then scores a basket.

Backboard: The rectangular structure behind and at the top of the basketball net. Players will often bounces the ball off the backboard and then into the net to score a basket.

Basket: The basket is attached to the backboard and is through which points are scored by getting the ball to travel through it. The basket consists of a circular metal rim with rope mesh that hangs down from it. The rim is 18" in diameter and is suspended 10' from the floor. (Also refers to a successful field-goal, "he scored a basket")

Blocked shot: When a player on defense knocks or deflects the ball with his hand after a player shoots the ball toward the basket, preventing a field goal.

Chest pass: When a player passes the ball to a team mate by starting from a chest position and then propelling the ball with both hands by extending his arms quickly.

Court: The area where a basketball game is played, bounded by 2 sidelines and 2 end lines, having a basket at each end.

Defensive rebound: When a defensive player gains control of the ball after a missed shot, a rebound occurs when the ball bounces off the rim or backboard.

Double team: When two teammates surround and guard an opponent, trying to steal the ball from him or prevent the player from making a pass.

Dribble or dribbling: When a player with the ball wants to move his position on the floor, he must dribble the ball, bouncing it off the floor as he moves his feet to advance the ball and keeping control of it.

Field goal: When a shot is made and the ball enters the basket from above, it is worth 2 points, or 3 points if the shooter was standing behind the 3-point line.

Floor violation: When a player's action breaks a rule but does not prevent an opponent's movement or cause him harm. The referee awards the ball to the opposing team as a penalty. An example of a floor violation is when a player is caught travelling. (see travelling)

Foul: When a player's action breaks a rule of the game, a penalty is enforced by the referee in a change in possession or free-throw at the basket in favor of the other team.

Free-throw: An opportunity for a player to take a free (unguarded) shot from the foul line after a foul was committed by an opponent. Each free is worth 1 point. (a personal or technical foul)

Guarding: When a player follows an opponent with the ball around the court to prevent him from dribbling close to the basket, taking an open shot or making a pass, also guarding is following a player without the ball to prevent him from receiving a pass.

Half-court press: When defenders start guarding the players starting to go on offense right away after a basket has been scored.

Jump shot: When a player jumps up with possession of the ball, then aims and shoots to score a basket while still in the air.

Key: The painted area on the floor at each end of the court in front of the basket.

Layup or layin: A shot taken by a player after dribbling to the basket. They then leap towards the basket and using one hand they drop the ball directly into the basket, a layin, or they bounce the ball off the backboard into the basket, a layup.

Loose ball: A ball that is not in the possession of any player during play.

Net: The netting attached to the frame of the goal to trap the puck when a goal is scored.

Offensive rebound: When an offensive player gains control of the ball after a missed shot, a rebound occurs when the ball bounces off the rim or backboard.

Overtime: An extra period of play used when the game is tied after regulation time has run out.

Pass: When a player throws the ball to a teammate. It is used to start plays, move the ball down the court and keep it away from defenders. Players will pass the ball around until one players feels he can take a good shot at the basket.

Personal foul: When contact, that may result in harm or injury, is made between two players that gives one team an unfair advantage during a play. Players may not push, hold, trip, hack, elbow, restrain or charge into an opponent or a foul will be called.

Pivot: When a stationary player with the ball, turns looking to pass or shoot the ball, his one foot must remain touching the floor until he passes or shoots the ball.

Possession: When a player has the ball in his hands and is in control of it, his team has possession.

Rebound: After a missed shot, a rebound occurs when the ball bounces off the rim or backboard. All the players will try to grab the ball that has bounced off the rim or backboard after a missed shot to gain possession of the ball. (see offensive rebound and defensive rebound)

Referees: The officials in a basketball game. They watch all the action closely to make sure all the rules are followed so the game is played fairly. They watch for and call any fouls and make decisions about field-goals scored.

Score: When a player shoots, lays-in, lays-up, slam-dunks or tips the basketball into the basket of the opposing team for a field-goal. (a field-goal is worth two points)

Slam dunk: When a player close to the basket jumps up and reaches above the basket and then strongly pushes the ball down into the basket quickly.

Team fouls: Each personal foul committed by a player is also counted against his team. When a team goes over the limit, its opponent is awarded free-throw opportunities.

Technical foul: The referee can call a technical foul against players or coaches for unsportsmanlike conduct during a game. Free throws are awarded to the opposing team.

3-point shot: A field goal is worth 3 points when the shooter has both feet on the floor behind the 3-point line when he released the ball, also counts if one foot is behind the line while the other is in the air.

travelling: When a player with the ball takes too many steps without dribbling, he must be bouncing the ball off the floor if he wants move around the court for a better position. (also called walking) The opposing team is awarded the ball as when a travelling occurs.

Turnover: When the offense loses possession of the ball through its own fault by passing the ball out of bounds or committing a floor violation.

Literacy Guide Chart

Practice early reading skills using the special page format.
-The special page format is designed for children to practice key skills in their reading development.
-The story text is in black, and the alphabet letters in blue on the left, with story words in red on the right.
-This is a handy reference to practice some early reading skills, before, during or after reading the story.

4 Building Blocks Of Reading - With Suggested Reading Skills Activities
-The chart below highlights 4 specific skills that are key building blocks required to produce a new reader.
Use their current ability as a guide to focus on the appropriate skills to practice.

1
Oral Language Development

Speaking aloud and expressing ideas and thoughts builds oral language skills and provides an essential foundation for the development of reading.

Suggested Activities

- look through the story letting the child talk and tell about the pictures using their own words

- encourage, listen and actively respond to the child's own words, thoughts and ideas

-prompt for more oral discussion and detail with questions and rephrasing their words and ideas

-take turns talking about the action and what the players and fans might be feeling, thinking and saying

2
Letter and Sound Recognition

An essential pre-reading skill is recognizing all the letters (upper and lower case) of the alphabet and the sounds that they make.

Suggested Activities

- together point to each blue letter, name and make the sound of each letter in the alphabet

- explain letters have a lower case (small) symbol and upper case (big) symbol

- name a letter, the sound it makes and then have your child point to it (take turns making it a fun game)

- identify a letter and see if it can be found in a red word on the left and in the story (letters make words)

3
Building Word Vocabulary

An important reading skill development is the ability to visually identify words, to recognize the grouping of letters and to remember the word meaning.

Suggested Activities

- point to and say a red word, name each letter and their sounds that group together making each word

- point to and read a red word and then let your child find it in the story sentence (take turns making it a game)

- take turns pointing to and reading aloud each red word from the top to bottom in order

- point to a red word, have your child say the word and explain its meaning (make a sentence with the word)

4
Reading Fluency and Comprehension

Developing the ability to read words accurately and understand their meaning at the same time produces a fluent and competent reader.

Suggested Activities

- read the story together, develop a rhythm and use the rhyme to create and model a natural reading fluency

-ask questions about the action and events to check for memory and understanding

- discuss the thinking, emotions and feelings of the many players and spectators watching the game

- talk about team work, fair-play and sportsmanship, allowing your child to express their feelings and ideas

Find a good balance between working with a child's current abilities and challenging them to learn!
Support literacy development!

Sports Action Kids Books - Book 4
ISBN-978-1-7771741-9-4

sportsactionbooks@gmail.com

Copyright © Coach Craig B.Ed. 2020

Made in the USA
Las Vegas, NV
13 December 2020